101 Ways to Stop Being Bored!

101 Ways to Stop Being Bored!

By Malcolm with David Levithan

SCHOLASTIC INC.

New York   Toronto   London   Auckland
Sydney   Mexico City   New Delhi
Hong Kong   Buenos Aires

ISBN 0-439-49170-3

12 11 10 9 8 7 6 5 4 3 2 1   3 4 5 6 7 8/0

Printed in the U.S.A.

First printing, January 2003

To Billy, Chris, Anica, Eireann, and Savannah
(for a most un-boring summer) – DL

101 Ways to Stop Being Bored!

INTRODUCTION

There's nothing worse than being bored. Like when there's nothing good on TV or when you're sitting in class and you feel like you have to punch yourself in the ear just to stay awake. Or when Mom's been yelling at you for so long all you hear is "blah blah blah."

In my family, things rarely calm down long enough to be boring. But other people are not so "lucky." For them, I have come up with a few suggestions to help cope with those moments of extreme boredom.

HOW TO ~~AVOID~~ BEING ~~BORED~~ IN ENGLISH CLASS

I love the English language. I use it to yell at my brothers all the time. But English class doesn't help me much in that area. Here are some ways to keep English class from being a total snooze fest.

- Pretend to mishear things. Like when the teacher is talking about Elizabethan theater, say, "Shakes beer? Who shakes beer?"

- Make up limericks about the people you know. Here's one from the other day:

  There once was a boy named Reese,
  Who wasn't a man of peace.
  He would roll in the mud
  To deliver a thud,
  And his hair was full of grease.

- Make up your own spelling bee. That way you can tell the big idiot in the front row that he's a N-E-A-N-D-E-R-T-H-A-L without him having a chance of figuring it out.

- Pass notes that include literary quotations. That way, if you're caught, you can claim it was part of the assignment.

- Answer all your teacher's questions in Spanish or French. Just to see if she notices.

HOW TO TURN YOUR HOMEWORK INTO A SOURCE OF ENDLESS AMUSEMENT

If you do an hour of homework a day for every day you're in school, by the time you graduate, you've wasted ninety days of your life. That's three whole months your teachers have stolen from you. Here are some suggestions on how to make that time your own.

- Bring on the noise. Listening to music while you work might just keep you awake long enough to finish. And if it's loud enough, your mom might not want to encourage any more studying.

- Do your homework on the phone with a friend. Misery loves company.

- Do your science experiments in the kitchen and see if your family accidentally mistakes them for dinner. My dad was halfway through a tall, cool glass of swampy terrarium water before he realized it.

✒ Get your brothers to help. When I study for vocabulary quizzes, I make flash cards. When I learn a word, I let Dewey eat the card. That way, everyone's happy.

✒ Ask your parents for help. They pretend math's important, but they don't remember it, either. See if you can get them frustrated enough to admit they have never used the magic of trigonometry in their everyday lives.

OTHER WAYS TO SURVIVE A BORING CLASS

HOW TO SURVIVE A BORING TEACHER

Teachers know a lot of things, but they're never able to explain why you should care. It may feel like you have to stab a pencil in your thigh to stay awake in class, but here are some things you should try first.

- Doodle. I prefer doodling with a pencil, but my brother Dewey is a mixed-media doodler. He's currently exploring ear wax.

- Leave strange objects on the teacher's desk. Flowers? Cookies? She'll be happy for the rest of the day. Insects? That's asking for extra homework. But an "Iowa is for lovers" magnet? She won't know what to think.

- Play Classroom Bingo. Fill the squares with words the teacher always uses. Each time

GO TO YOUR ROOM RIGHT NOW!	REESE!	I DIDN'T DO IT!
BOYS!	I THINK DEWEY'S GOING TO BE SICK!	HAL!!
DEWEY, TAKE THAT OUT OF YOUR MOUTH.	REESE, PUT YOUR BROTHER DOWN!	DON'T GIVE ME THAT LOOK!

she uses a phrase, put an X through it.
First one with three in a row wins. (Above
is a sample of the home game.)

✒ Track the teacher's clothing choices.
Does she really only have one outfit or
do they all just look the same?

Pretend you're on a TV show. Whenever the teacher cracks a lame joke, convince the whole class to laugh uproariously.

THINGS TO DO DURING BORING TV COMMERCIALS

Some commercials are better than the shows. Like the ones with snowboarders or talking dogs. But other commercials give television a bad name. My brothers and I have come up with a few ways to get through the slow spots without ever leaving the couch.

- Argue with the commercial. For every phrase they use, say the opposite. If something's "new and improved," say "old and just as bad." If a movie is "a triumph of the human spirit," say it's "a failure of the canine bladder."

- Channel surf competitively. Start clicking through the channels and see how close you can get to coming back to the original channel before the commercial is over.

Whoever gets the closest without going over wins.

- Overdubbing. When a stupid commercial comes on, put the TV on mute and make up your own words. For example, take a men's hair-care ad: "Yeah, I used to be bald, but then I trained a small, furry rodent to sleep on my head. Now, I'm a babe magnet . . . If I could only get rid of the smell.

- Do the soda jerk. Every time a soda commercial comes on, see how many times you can burp before the commercial's over.

- Argue over who gets the remote control. This adds a physical element to your television watching.

THINGS TO DO ON A SATURDAY NIGHT BESIDES STAYING HOME AND WATCHING TV

For some reason, people think Saturday night is the time to go out and have fun. Don't they know Cops is on? But if you decide you don't want to stay home and watch TV, here are some other things to do on a Saturday night.

- Go over to a friend's house to watch TV.

- Go to a restaurant or pizza place that has a TV.

- Get a long extension cord and sneak the TV into your backyard. (Don't try this in the rain. Trust me on this one.)

- Get some friends together and act out your favorite TV show.

✎ <u>Ask a girl out on a date</u>... to a restaurant or pizza place that has a TV.

HOW TO AVOID BEING BORED ON A FIELD TRIP TO A MUSEUM

I am all for art appreciation. Especially if it gets me a day off of school. One teacher watching thirty kids means plenty of opportunities to liven up the place.

- Whenever you go into the Egyptian exhibit, yell, "I want my mummy!" See how the museum guard reacts.

- In the dinosaur section, taunt the fossils by saying, "What are you staring at?" See how the museum guard reacts.

- In the art gallery, put your head down between your knees and look at each painting upside down. See how the museum guard reacts.

✎ In the portrait gallery, have staring contests with the paintings. See how the museum guard reacts.

✎ Buy a postcard in the gift shop, then
head back to the exhibits and ask the
guard for an autograph. If he hasn't
thrown you out yet, this just might do it.

UN-BORING THINGS TO DO WITH YOUR BEST FRIEND

My best friend Stevie is in a wheelchair and can't do anything without running . . . out . . . of . . . breath. You'd think that would make things dull, but we have a great time together. Here are some of the un-boring things we do.

- Race each other. We like to turn the school hallway into a NASCAR track. We were racing once, and Stevie made the kid pushing the AV cart spin out into the wall. That was cool.

- Get revenge on nonhandicapped people who park in handicapped parking spaces. It's a little embarrassing to come back from grabbing a video and find Stevie — wheelchair and all — sitting on the hood of your car.

- Make your own comic book. Stevie's a comic-book nut, so his superhero is called The Mint Condition Avenger. He punishes evildoers who crease pages or fold covers.

- Pick a charity and go door-to-door collecting for it. We do really well. Believe me, after years of practice with his parents, Stevie knows how to work the guilt.

- Take on the school bully. As Stevie showed me once, there are some things (like picking on a kid like Stevie) that can turn a big threat into a big dork in no time.

HOW TO AVOID BEING BORED WHEN YOU'RE CLOTHES SHOPPING IN THE MALL

If it were up to me, I'd never shop for new clothes. They're just going to get torn and dirty anyway. Unfortunately, my mom doesn't share my philosophy. Here's how I survive a trip to the mall.

- Convince the shoe salesperson that you have a prosthetic foot and he has to be extra careful or it will fall off.

- Try to convince your brothers that something really uncool is the latest trend. I once got Reese to buy pink golf pants. On the plus side, one of the cafeteria ladies said he reminded her of her dead husband.

- Go to the info desk and demand information like, "What were the lasting accomplishments of Franklin Pierce's presidency?" or "Is everything big in Texas?"

- If you're a boy, shove a beach ball down your shirt. Go to the maternity section and watch the look on the salesperson's face as you ask to try on some of the clothes.

- Have a contest to find the ugliest outfit possible. (Do not try this if you are shopping with your mother. She'll probably like the outfit and make you wear it for real.)

THINGS TO DO ON A DATE THAT AREN'T TOTALLY BORING

I'm not exactly a dating expert, so I went to my family for help on this one.

- According to my mom, I should treat the girl I'm with like she's special. I should open the door for her, listen to her, do what she wants to do . . . Wait a minute! This is supposed to be a book about things that <u>aren't</u> boring.

- According to my dad, I should take a girl out for a malted (whatever that is) and then to a horror movie. When she gets scared, she'll jump right into my arms. You know, like the way Dad hugs Mom when he's frightened.

- According to Francis, the most romantic date is traveling over a thousand miles to see a girl you've been writing cheesy love letters to. Of course, his girl ended up dumping him, but he said maybe it will work out better for me.

- According to Reese, his perfect date would be watching <u>Wrestlemania</u> on TV while the girl brought him snacks. That'll happen.

- According to Dewey, a date is any time a girl doesn't hit you and say go away.

(Okay, so maybe nobody in my family's an expert.)

WAYS TO STAY ~~ATTENTIVE~~ IN ~~AN~~ EMERGENCY ROOM

My family is no stranger to the emergency room. Whether it's Reese fighting or Dewey sticking things up his nose or Dad getting his tongue stuck in a conch shell (don't ask), we always seem to find our way to the ER. Here are some ways to entertain yourself while the doctor is examining your brother.

- Do yourself up in gauze, wrapping it around your head mummy-style. Then head to the cafeteria and ask people if they've seen your nose lying around any-where.

- Switch the covers on the year-old maga-zines. Watch for the guy who picks up a copy of Men's Health and gets a copy of Seventeen instead. See if he keeps read-ing.

✦ Sing along with the Muzak. The louder you get, the quicker the doctor will come.

✦ Doctors and nurses love it when you say, "But that's not the way they do it on <u>ER</u>!" Watch the colors they turn the more times you say it. Ask to see Doctor Carter.

✦ <u>Stretcher races.</u> When you're injured, you never really get to appreciate the way they handle.

HOW TO AVOID BEING BORED ON A LONG CAR RIDE

A lot of the time it doesn't feel like our house is big enough for our family. Now, imagine us in a car for more than five minutes. Without air-conditioning. This is how my family gets through long car rides.

- I Spy. We try to be creative. Instead of spying cars and trees, we do things like, "I spy a really fat person trying to snarf down an ice cream cone in one bite" or "I spy two people in the car next to us having a huge argument over folding the map."

- Backseat warfare. All's fair as long as you do not, whatever you do, kick the back of Mom's seat. She will turn this car around.

✏️ <u>Bathroom warfare.</u> Wait until everyone has had a Coke at the rest stop. Then, an hour or so later, start talking about waterfalls, dams breaking, waves crashing . . . and see who's the first to yell "Pull over!"

- Try to find the town with the strangest name. Purgatory? Hazard? Dead Horse? Why can't we live somewhere cool like that?

- Name That Tune. Skip around the radio dial and see who can name the most songs in one go-round. The loser has to sing along with the next song. Even if it's opera. Especially if it's opera.

HOW TO ~~AVOID BEING~~ BORED WHEN YOUR ~~FATHER IS TALKING TO YOU ABOUT MANLY~~ THINGS

You know the conversations where your dad pulls you aside and talks to you about "Being a Man." It's awkward for you. It's awkward for him. You don't have the heart to tell him you know all this already. And he's getting a few things wrong. In this case, I suggest you just play along. These questions should humor him.

✎ Gee, Dad, what was your first kiss like? (My father's answer: "It was at a party. The lights were dim. The candles were lit. Well, three candles were lit. She was three, I was two. She leaned right over and kissed me. I will never forget how I cried.")

✎ But Dad, what's the right way to treat a girl? ("Like a woman, son, like a woman.")

- How do you know if a girl's the right one?
("Well, in your mother's case, she told me.)

- If you like a girl, should you call her right
away or should you wait a few days? ("You
can wait?")

- Does it matter what a girl's sign is? ("Absolutely not. Unless she says her sign is
'Trespassers will be prosecuted.'")

HOW TO ~~AVOID~~ BEING ~~BORED~~ WHEN YOUR MOTHER IS LAYING DOWN THE LAW

My mom yells at us so much, I can't tell where the lectures start and stop anymore. This is how I suggest you get through a scolding.

- Look her right in the eye and don't, whatever you do, let her realize you're bored.

- Nod meaningfully and don't, whatever you do, let her realize you're bored.

- Appear apologetic and don't, whatever you do, let her realize you're bored.

Repeat (1) through (3) and DON'T, WHAT-
EVER YOU DO, LET HER REALIZE YOU'RE
BORED. I CANNOT STRESS THAT ENOUGH.

HOW TO AVOID BEING BORED WHILE RIDING ON THE SCHOOL BUS

The wheels on the bus go round and round . . . and so can your head if you're trapped on board for too long. Here are some things to do to make a bus ride special.

- Check out the driver's reaction after you convince the younger kids on the bus that blowing on each red light will make it turn green. Watch them turn blue.

- Patiently explain to the driver that the bus is unsafe because of the lack of seatbelts. The only responsible thing to do is to forget about going to school, stop the bus right now and let everyone out.

- Yell the same thing from the street after you've been banned from the bus.

✐ Sing-alongs are fun. Especially when you get everyone but your least favorite person on the bus to stop singing at the same time giving Reese an unexpected solo.

✐ Here's one I learned from Francis. Set up a school bus betting pool. Take odds on how many Chevys you'll pass or how late you'll be to school. Play craps in the aisles.

HOW TO AVOID BEING BORED WHEN ACTING AS A TREE IN THE SCHOOL PLAY

Let's face it. There are small parts. They're the ones with less lines. My brothers have had long careers playing roles like "Servant," "Soldier #4" and "Second Tree on the Left." Reese hates to let the leads have all the attention. He's found several ways to enjoy himself even when he's playing shrubbery.

- Be helpful. Feed the other actors their lines.

- Be not so helpful. Feed the actors more entertaining fake lines.

- When there's a dramatic pause, yell "TIM-BER" and fall sideways onto the stage.

✏ Get the other trees to sway back and forth as if a wind were blowing on stage. Hit Our Town with a sudden hurricane.

✏ Convince the teacher you can be the tree while still wearing your street clothes.

FIVE THINGS IN A SCIENCE CLASSROOM THAT CAN PREVENT YOU FROM BEING TOTALLY BORED

Unfortunately, science class isn't always about blowing stuff up. If you're creative, though, there are plenty of things in the science classroom to keep your interest.

- Creatures. Animals weren't meant to be kept in cages. Or in Room 113A. Liberate them. See if the hamster and the lizard can be friends.

- Beakers. Bring in some Mountain Dew and pour it into your beaker. Watch the teacher freak out when you drink your new "discovery."

- Surgical tubing. Good for tying up your brothers, launching spitballs or, when combined with a funnel, constructing a giant slingshot.

- Magnets. See if you can lead that kid with braces around the room.

- Bunsen burners. Fire? In school? What were they thinking?

WAYS TO BREAK THE BORING LUNCH ROUTINE

Now, don't get me wrong. Lunch is the best part of the school day. But sometimes it can get a little old. Sitting with the same people, eating the same "food." Here are some ways to spice things up.

- Swap lunches. Find a friend who has a better lunch than you. Sit down next to him and say, "Hey, let's switch." Starting with the dessert, get your hands, mouth and saliva all over his food before he realizes what's happened.

- Food fights. These can get you into trouble, but only if they catch you starting it.

- Tray hockey. The tray is your stick and some piece of food is your puck. Clear the whole table and set up a goal on each

end. The trick is to prevent the puck
from flying off the table . . . and into one
of the lunchroom supervisors.

- Get the cafeteria ladies on your side. Ask
them about their children. Always say
thank you. If their hair nets look especially nice, tell them so. When they realize
you're actually being nice to them, you'll
eat like a king.

- Set an animal loose in the cafeteria. It'll
be fun, plus if it dies after eating some
of the cafeteria food, it's done you a
service.

HOW TO AVOID BEING BORED WHEN YOU'RE STUCK IN RIGHT FIELD

It happens to all of us. Well, all of us who aren't that good. Right Field. The planet Pluto of gym-time baseball. With the kids in my class, it's more likely that one of them will hit themselves in the mouth with the bat than hit one straight into right. But that doesn't mean you can't liven up your time in no-man's-land.

- Get into a staring contest with the centerfielder. Loser has to sing "Take Me Out to the Ball Game" at the top of his lungs. You probably don't want to do this during a play.

- Bait the gym teacher. Gym teachers may have been high school stars once, but now they take out all their aggression on their whistles. See how many toots you

can get out of them. Fielding from a
deck chair usually gets their attention.

- Plan elaborate revenge on the opposing
team. It doesn't matter whether you win
or lose — it's how bad you can get back at
them.

- See everything in terms of math. Check
out the angle of the swing, the velocity
of the ball, the probability of the batter
actually making contact ... I know it's
geeky, but if you were cool, you wouldn't
be in right field.

- Count blades of grass. It sounds boring,
but with a little sun stroke, it gets kind of
Zen.

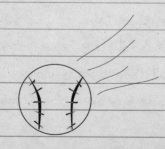

HOW TO ~~AVOID BEING~~ BORED WHEN YOUR MOM TAKES YOU ~~AND~~ YOUR LITTLE ~~BROTHER~~ TO THE SUPERMARKET

Grocery shopping is not my mom's favorite thing. She approaches it like a general going into battle: get in and get out as fast as you can and minimize the casualties. That doesn't mean Dewey and I can't have some fun.

- Rearrange aisle seven by color. Coke, tomato sauce and Tide all in one spot? Why not?

- Taste whatever you can. Nobody's going to miss one grape from a bunch. But don't get greedy. When Dewey stole a water-melon, they found a very sick boy at the end of the trail of seeds.

- Read the magazines by the checkout counter. Want some good fiction? Try the story about the 300-pound baby living in Corpus Christi or the dinosaur girl going to middle school in Gainesville.

- Compete with your brother in a game of "What is the Most Ridiculous Thing We Can Convince Mom to Buy?" Can we get Mom to spring for the new peanut butter-strawberry-marshmallow-grape cereal? Be careful, though. If your mom's anything like mine, she'll actually make you eat it. All of it.

- Utilize technology. Swipe your brother over the price scanner and see how much he's worth.

HOW TO ~~AVOID BEING~~ BORED WHEN YOUR ~~DAD~~ TAKES YOU TO THE SUPERMARKET

My mom usually knows better than to send Dad to the supermarket unsupervised. Let's just say he gets easily distracted. Here are some ways for me to guarantee that any grocery trip with my dad is an exciting one.

- Convince him to shop alphabetically. Aspirin first, then beef, then the chips and so on. (The catsup/ketchup controversy did slow us down a little bit, though.)

- Tell him that some of the aisles are haunted. Once, I told my dad the story of the poor eight-year-old who died in aisle eleven after he tried to pull the bottom roll of toilet paper out first and was crushed by the resulting avalanche. My dad was so spooked he didn't buy toilet paper for weeks.

- Shopping cart races. Subtract points for knocking down people or displays. Bonus points for picking up your groceries while you race.

- There is no such game as "What is the Most Ridiculous Thing We Can Convince Dad to Buy?" It's too easy. So instead we play "What is the Most Ridiculous Thing We Can Convince Dad to Buy Without Mom Killing Us When We Get Home?"

- Utilize technology. Get your dad to scan himself and see how much he's worth.

THINGS MY MOM DOES TO ~~AVOID~~ BEING ~~BORED~~ IN THE KITCHEN

Some moms love to cook. They whip up fancy dishes. They have heard of other cheeses besides American. Every meal is an adventure. Well, in my house, meals are still an adventure — but in a "risk your life" kind of way. Here's how Mom tries to keep things interesting in the kitchen.

- Disguising leftovers. Smother last night's dinner in ketchup and it's a whole new meal.

- International nights. Smother last night's dinner in salsa and it's a whole new meal.

- Special ingredients. This means whatever's on sale. We're still recovering from the week the local supermarket got an extra load of bananas. For days, we were having

banana bread, banana fritters, banana
burgers, banana stir fry . . .

🪶 The more the merrier. If Mom's going to
have to slave away in the kitchen, she's
going to make us help.

🪶 The more the messier. It usually takes
about two minutes for Mom to realize it's
a bad idea to have any of us in the
kitchen with her. Before we know it, she's
telling us to GET OUT OF THE KITCHEN
THIS INSTANT!

THINGS MY ~~DAD DOES~~ TO ~~AVOID BEING~~ BORED IN THE KITCHEN

Mom doesn't allow Dad to cook, but he does have to keep her company. This is what he does to stay awake.

- Talk to the shaker people. Dad likes to think of the salt and pepper shakers as a married couple. He makes them talk to each other. Sometimes they argue and throw salt and pepper at each other, but in the end, they always make up. Or Mom takes them away.

- Rearrange the kitchen magnets to see if they contain hidden messages.

- If the right Motown song comes on the radio, Dad will do the dance of the seven dish towels.

- Count the tiles. This is what Mom tells him to do when he starts to distract her with his dancing.

- Make lemon squares. They're the only food that my dad knows how to make. He bakes hundreds of them and tries to convince us they make the perfect breakfast, lunch, dinner or midnight snack.

THINGS I WOULD DO TO AVOID ~~BOREDOM~~ IF I ~~HAD~~ MOM'S JOB

My mom works at a big drugstore. She claims she's never been tempted to raid the pharmacy, but I would go crazy if I had that job. Here's what I would do to stay sane.

✒ Guess the life histories of the customers by what they buy. That guy checking out with a plastic bottle of vodka, a pot pie and some kitty litter — there's a story there. A sad story.

✒ Answer the phone in different voices. You'd trust a pharmacist who sounded like Tweety Bird, wouldn't you?

✒ Try to convince the customer that they absolutely, positively must have an item you know they absolutely, positively don't need. Like selling a hair brush to a bald man.

✦ Page famous people over the intercom
  and watch everyone rubbernecking to see
  if Keanu Reeves is really going to go clean
  up aisle two.

✦ Raid the candy aisle. Why would they give
  you two Twix if you weren't supposed to
  sandwich another candy bar in between
  them?

HOW TO AVOID BOREDOM BY INVENTING A NEW OLYMPIC SPORT

This is my dad's specialty — turning his quirks into what he calls "the next international pastime." Here are my father's top five boredom-busting sports.

- LP-licking. While blindfolded, my dad can identify every one of the dusty old records in his collection by feeling the grooves on the LP with his tongue. If this were an Olympic sport, he would be a champion. Mainly, because no one else is weird enough to do it.

- Egg golf. You have to be very gentle. But like they say, you can't play egg golf without breaking some eggs.

- Fence fencing. Grab a couple pickets from an old fence and knock yourself out. (Hopefully, not literally.)

- The toilet paper endurance-a-thon. See how close you can get to the end of a toilet paper roll without actually finishing it off and having to replace it. Even if you only use up half a sheet . . . or an eighth . . . or a hundredth . . . you get the picture.

- Figure shaking. Roller boogie back from Burger Barn carrying a milk shake. If you make it home without covering yourself in shake, then you're ready for the gold.

THINGS MY BROTHER FRANCIS DOES TO KEEP FROM BEING BORED IN ~~ALASKA~~

When Francis was in Alaska, he had to make his own fun. This is what he did to keep his blood warm.

- Think of creative ways to blame Mom for everything. When he almost choked on a piece of moose steak, he said it was all Mom's fault because she's so controlling, she cut his meat too small when he was little and didn't prepare him for the real world. He's a genius at this.

- Salmon tossing.

- Snow angel contests. According to Francis, the real pros do it naked.

- Play hockey. According to Francis, the real pros do it naked.

Get married. Boy, I hope I'm never that bored.

THINGS MY BROTHER REESE DOES TO AVOID BEING BORED AT AN OLD AGE HOME

Okay, it's not like Reese would volunteer to go visit old people, but he has to fill his hours of community service somehow. The nursing home residents are always glad to see him: they're glad to see anybody. This is how Reese tries to make things a little more exciting.

- Talk to the veterans about all their war stories — then rearrange the cafeteria so you and the guys can act them out. Last week, they stormed the dessert cart.

- Dance with the ladies. They tip.

- Collect bedpans. You never know when you'll need them for pranks at school.

✼ Start a black market for decent food.
Smuggle in a couple Twinkies and a hamburger and you can make a fortune.

✼ Introduce the residents to new music. You
haven't really lived until you've seen a
ninety-year-old woman rock out to Nirvana.

WAYS MY BROTHER REESE KEEPS RECESS ACTIVE

Some people like to sit around after they eat. Let things digest. Not my brother Reese. He's designed a full workout program for some of the smaller and weaker kids at lunchtime to keep them active and fit.

- Running. Reese likes to motivate the kids by shouting out encouraging phrases like "I'm going to make your life a steaming hot plate of misery."

- Obstacle course. If you don't want to be put in the garbage can, you better jump over it.

- Yoga. Reese finds inner peace by bending other kids' bodies into painful positions.

- Wrestling. Greco-Roman, WWF - Reese knows all the moves.

✦ Fetch. Reese likes to throw little kids'
books and school supplies onto the audito-
rium roof and watch them climb up to re-
trieve them. They never learn, though.
Once they fetch, Reese just throws the
stuff back up there again.

DAD'S ARTS AND CRAFTS PROJECTS

Sometimes we complain to Dad that we're bored. He says how can you be bored when there's so many fun things to do. We say, like what? He looks around trying to think of something and then attempts to convince us that some household item is really entertaining. Last time, it was a roll of string. Here's his ideas for string art.

- Make friendship bracelets. He hasn't noticed that we aren't girls.

- Tie everything in the room together. It's fun to see who will be the first person to open the front door and pull down a book case.

- Tie a piece of string around your finger to remind you to do something. Then tie

another piece on your finger to remind
you what that first piece is for. Then tie
another piece on your finger to remind
you what that one is for . . .

✍ Become one with the string. Tie a piece
of string to Dewey and have him run in
and out of the house over and over
again. Dad calls it the Human Yo-yo.

✍ Make macramé plant holders. Dad says
they were totally cool during the seven-
ties. Those were dark times.

DEWEY'S ARTS AND CRAFTS PROJECTS

Dewey is a big fan of using household objects as arts and crafts supplies. The results are very, um, inventive. And they usually have to be cleaned up before Mom gets home.

✒ For Dewey, bouquets aren't about flowers at all. Mom came home the other day to find a brilliant new centerpiece on the kitchen table — two toilet plungers, three unwound hangers, and four carrots arranged in a vase that "belonged to her great-grandmother and has been lovingly handed down over the generations, and did we have any idea what would happen to us if it broke?"

✒ Potato sculpture. With a plastic knife and safety scissors, Dewey has carved potatoes into the shape of eyeballs, Mount

Rushmore and . . . a potato. That was from his experimental period.

- Pillow dressing. Dewey likes to "borrow" other people's clothes and turn his pillow into a friend. And you wonder why he has trouble making real ones?

- Soap carving. Kind of the same as potato sculpture, only here, Dewey eats his creations.

- Candy mosaics. Dewey uses half-chewed and half-sucked pieces of candy to create amazing patterns. His masterwork is a self-portrait done entirely out of half-eaten Life Savers. It's currently stuck to the bottom of our couch.

MOM'S ~~ARTS AND~~ CRAFTS PROJECTS

I asked Mom for creative arts and crafts projects, but I'm not quite sure she got into the spirit of the idea.

✔ "How 'bout you go and make your bed creatively?"

✔ "Wash the dishes creatively."

✔ "Do your homework creatively."

✔ "Clean your room creatively."

✔ "Take the garbage out creatively."

REESE'S ARTS AND CRAFTS PROJECTS

I never realized my brother was such an artist. Here are some of his arts and crafts projects.

🖋 Mud masks. Push some little kid's face in the mud until his imprint is left there. Sometimes you can still see his scream.

🖋 Cast decoration. Reese has had his share of broken bones. Sometimes he'll use a red marker to make it look like his cast is bleeding. Other times, he'll scrawl messages like "YOU'RE NEXT!" So far, no one has ever signed "Get Well."

🖋 Roof ornamentation. Reese likes decorating roofs with other people's things, like book bags, lunches, baseballs and, if he's really inspired, underwear.

- Human sculpture. Reese will go up to some- one who's scared of him and yell "FREEZE!" in a very intimidating way. The kid won't move for hours . . . not if he knows what's good for him.

- Quilting. Reese really likes to stitch. Just don't tell him I told you . . . I'm serious. <u>Don't</u> tell him I told you.

OTHER BOREDOM BUSTERS

Did I forget anything? What are some other things you do to avoid being bored?

HOW TO ~~AVOID~~ BEING ~~BORED~~ WHEN YOU'RE STUCK IN ~~A~~ BORING ~~ASSEMBLY~~

Sleeping in class is fun, but snoring in front of the entire school is embarrassing. What should I do to stay awake?

HOW TO HANDLE A SLOW VISIT FROM YOUR GRANDPARENTS

Of course, my grandparents are on the loud side. But I've heard that other grandparents like to nap a lot and watch TV shows starring people even older than they are. What are some things you can do to improve the visit?

THINGS TO DO DURING
A BORING MOVIE

There's nothing worse than going to the movie theater and being stuck watching a boring film. It's not like you can change the channel. There have to be other ways to keep things interesting. Any suggestions?

KEEP TRACK OF YOUR
FAVORITE WAYS FOR
STOPPING BOREDOM —
YOU NEVER KNOW WHEN
YOU MIGHT NEED
THEM!